Most of us can look at our lives and notic̶ ̶ ̶ ̶ ̶ ̶ ̶ ̶ ̶ ̶ ̶ ̶ ̶ ̶ ̶ ̶o that we neglected to learn during our maturation̶ ̶ ̶ ̶ ̶ ̶ ̶ ̶ ̶ ̶ ̶ ̶ ̶ ̶ ̶ ̶ a few lessons; what we need is someone to re-parent us. Though it is impossible to physically become a child to learn missed lessons, re-parenting can occur with a wise mentor, a caring counselor, or in the case of the following story of young George, a truth fairy.

Although the following story is fictitious, if a certain President wants to claim that this is his biography, his dream, his impetus for transformation, I will gladly give him the credit he deserves.

NO, GEORGE, NO!

The RE-PARENTING of George W. Bush

Created by Kathy Eder
Illustrated by Clay Butler

A Primer for the Patriotic

Once upon a time, there was a man named George who was very tired. Even before the morning birds began singing, George had been awake signing papers, returning phone calls and making agreements with foreign diplomats. Clearly, George needed a nap. So he lay down on a soft couch in an oval office in his big, white house where he quickly fell asleep, and a vivid dream began to weave its magic.

In this dream, George's hands were little, his feet were little; indeed, his entire body was little, for the magic of dreams had turned George into a young boy.

And, in this dream the young boy George appeared to be mesmerized by a unique person who was leaping around and singing:

Anything is possible
Remember this is true,
Who you are becoming
Is entirely up to you.

GOT A STEADY JOB IN AN UNSTEADY ECONOMY? – *Center for American Progress,* by Sirota, Harvey and Legum, February 10, 2004 – ECONOMY: These Guys Just Don't Get It

"Who are you?" asked the young boy George.

"I'm the Truth Fairy, George. Only the very young can see and believe in me. Right now, I'm here to make sure that you learn a few lessons to carry with you throughout your life."

"What kind of lessons, Mr. Truf Fairy?"

"**Truth** Fairy, George. The first lesson, I suppose, is to focus on uttering **Truth**. You'll find that speaking **Truth** isn't always easy, George."

"Maybe my missing front teeth are the problem. I'll say it slowly. Trrruth Fairy. I did it! I spoke Truf! I mean Trrruth."

"Good boy, George. First lesson: Consistently speaking **Truth** requires commitment."

"So, George, would you like to play a game I call *Let's Imagine*? In this game, I'll ask you questions and then you will respond."

"Sure, I'll play! I love games, Mr. Truth Fairy."

"Okay, let's begin. Imagine that you have an important life ahead of you, George. When you grow up, you're going to be a leader in the United States…."

"Yahoo! I'm going to be King of the United States when I grow up! And the Supreme Court will be my court; they will choose me to be their King, and they will do everything I ask them to do."

"**NO, George, NO!** The U.S. has **NO KING!** And in the United States, it is the people, not the Supreme Court, who elect their leader, a President. And the Supreme Court is a non-biased group of judges that serves all people. So, let's imagine that you will be **PRESIDENT** one day, George. Who will elect you?"

GOT AN UNBIASED SUPREME COURT? www.findlaw.com – *The U.S. Supreme Court and The Imperial Presidency,* by John W. Dean, January 16, 2004

"Well, my friends will vote for me because I will make them rich and powerful when I'm King - I mean President."

"I see. You'll surround yourself with the wealthy. But, what about the hoi polloi, George?"

"Huh?"

"The masses of people, George, the regular folk who will elect you. What will you do for them?"

"Hmm. Well, I guess I need to be really, really nice to the U.S. people and promise them things before the election because after they vote for me, I'll have power, power, power! I can forget about the hoi polloi once they vote for me. I can be President forever and ever."

"But, George, in the United States, the President is re-elected every four years. What if the people don't re-elect you?"

"That's easy. Everyone will vote for me. Anyone who doesn't vote for me is a Boogeyman, anyway, and votes from Big Green Blobby Boogeymen don't count."

"You mean everyone who doesn't want you to be President is a Boogeyman whose vote doesn't count?"

"Exactly. I'll create voting machines and my powerful friends will make sure the machines only accept votes from my supporters. Votes from Boogeymen won't be counted! And I'll be in charge another four years."

"**NO, George, NO!** A President needs **INTEGRITY!** The U.S. people have a right to fair elections. A President must never use machines or powerful friends to manipulate votes. Presidents must be trustworthy."

GOT RICH FRIENDS WHO LIKE TO GIVE CAMPAIGN DONATIONS? — Center for Public Integrity, *U.S. Contractors Reap the Windfalls of Post-War Reconstruction*, by Beelman, October 30, 2003

GOT JOBS FOR YOUR FRIENDS? – The New Yorker, *Contract Sport*, by Jane Mayer, Feb 16 & 24, 2004

"But, I am trustworthy. My friends trust me. I always choose them for my team. And when I'm President, I'll give them special jobs. They can count on me."

"George, if you do this and ignore keeping your word with those who aren't your close friends, most of the wealth of this country will be under the control of your friends. Won't the other 99% of people in the United States be angry?"

"No one will be able to keep track of the money me and my friends earn. When we become rich, we're going to make gazillions of dollars like that company *Hellaburden*. And to avoid taxes, we'll put our money in the banks in the Cayman Islands."

"**NO, George, NO!** Companies like **Halliburton** who hide their money in the Cayman Islands hurt the U.S. economy. Why in the world would you and your wealthy friends want that much money, George?"

GOT TAX HAVENS? – *Perfectly Legal*, by David Cay Johnston, 2003

"So we can play **COPS AND ROBBERS** and fight wars all over the world! When I'm President, I'll gather all of the soldiers in the United States and give them really cool weapons and then we'll crush and destroy all of the bad guys all over the world!"

"Who are the bad guys, George?"

"Daddy's friends say bad guys are unpatriotic, unsupportive, complaining people. I call these people Boogeymen. Lurking beneath anyone who doesn't support me or my special plans is a Boogeyman. And these bad guys are everywhere."

"Wow! Boogeymen are everywhere, huh? And where will you get all of the soldiers needed to fight wars around the world?"

"Lots of people want to be soldiers. We'll feed them and clothe them and give them guns and a place to live while they fight. And we'll promise to take care of them when they live at home between all of the wars."

"I imagine if soldiers return home sick or injured you'll continue caring for them. Right?"

"No way, Mr. Truth Fairy! That's a waste of money! I won't keep someone on my team if they can't do what I want. And if any of those former soldiers complain, they're...."

"I know, George; all complainers are Boogeymen. Why would you want to fight these wars in the first place?"

"To get lots and lots of treasures for me and my friends."

"**NO, George, NO!** A great leader will never put soldiers in harm's way for selfish or unnecessary reasons. And, George, a truly great President keeps his promises. Your people will be so disappointed in you if you create wars for profit."

GOT SICK AND WOUNDED SOLDIERS? www.channel4.com/news – *The unseen cost of the war in Iraq*, by Jonathan Miller, February 10, 2004

"Well, actually, I'm very smart. You see, I won't tell the people in my country all about the wars."

"Would you lie, George?"

"Lying is wrong. I'll… I'll just hide the truth."

"How can you hide the truth about wars and people dying, George?"

"In **Hide 'N Go Seek**, good hiders know it's very important to hide in places where no one can find what they're looking for. So, I can make sure that my friends hide the news of wars from people who would find out in…in the **NEWS**. That's it! My friends will own the TV, and the radios, and the newspapers in the United States. Then, the news will only say what I want it to say!"

"Hiding the news and truth of wars from the world?"

"Exactly, Mr. Truth Fairy. And maybe my friends and me could be in charge of that famous TV station Daddy and his friends really like. It's called…um…I think it's called **FOE** news."

"**FAUX TV** news, George? That name doesn't seem like it would attract viewers."

"Well, it's something like that. Maybe it's called **FACTS TV** news."

"**FACTS TV** news certainly isn't a current U.S. TV station, George. Hmm. Let's see. A popular station? And FACTS is wrong? Oh, it must be **FAX TV** news, George."

"That's right! Their ads say **FAX TV**: *A fact similar of the truth.*"

"You mean **FAX TV: Where you get a Facsimile of the Truth**. Is that their motto, George?"

"Yes! Daddy watches FAX TV. He says everyone thinks they're getting real news, but they're really only learning what FAX TV wants them to hear. Me and my friends will operate FAX TV news when I'm President."

"But, George, what will you do if there are journalists who insist on asking you questions about real news or wars when you're President?"

"I'll just hold my breath or sing *Yankee Doodle Dandy* until the journalists go away."

"Fascinating! And how will you avoid discussing the deaths that happen in the wars, George?"

"That's easy. When anyone asks me about death, I'll do the *Hokey Pokey*, and I'll turn myself around and around until the journalists know that I don't want to talk about the deaths of anyone in war."

"No one? George, do you mean to say that you won't acknowledge the death of innocent civilians or soldiers?"

"Nope. Clever, huh? Avoiding journalists will be fun!"

"**NO, George, NO!** You must use your cleverness for doing what is right. The media can't be controlled like this. And families who lose loved ones in war might want our nation to grieve with them. A great leader will speak the truth and acknowledge the lives that have been lost. And by the way, George, a leader with good intelligence knows Boogeymen don't exist."

GOT ACKNOWLEDGEMENT OF THOSE DYING IN WAR? – Seattle Post Intelligencer, *Telling the Truth Won't Set You Free*, by Robert Fisk, November 27, 2003

"Have you ever seen a Boogeyman, Mr. Truth Fairy?"

"Of course not, George."

"Well, no one has, Mr. Truth Fairy, so I'll get my friends who own TV and radio and newspapers and we'll make up really scary stories about Green Blobby Boogeymen. And I'll create an organization to look for Boogeymen in the United States and all over the world."

"Let's imagine, George. What might you name this organization?"

"I could call it *The Powerful People and the U.S. Citizen's Taxes Running Our Lives to Protect Us.*"

"That's too long of a name, George. How about **Powerful and Taxes Running our Lives**? Say, George, why don't you use the letters from the beginning of the words and call your organization **P.A.T.R.O.L.**?"

"*PATROL*? That's just like the police are in charge of the country and the world! Cool! I love this game, Mr. Truth Fairy. I will call my organization *PATROL*."

GOT HOMELAND SECURITY THAT FEELS LIKE A POLICE STATE? – Daytona Beach News-Journal Online, *USA Patriot Act is Latest in Series of Bad Laws*, by Pierre Tristam, February 3, 2004

"And how will you get enough money to run **PATROL** and to chase the imaginary Boogeymen?"

"Well, my daddy says that if government services and tax money is ***pirate-ized***, there is lots of money for corporations."

"***Pirate-ized***? There's no such word as ***pirate-ized***, George. Let me think for a moment. Oh, you mean **privatized**. But, George, the U.S. taxes are needed in social programs. They're especially needed for regulations and protections for the environment and for those without work."

"Who cares about regulations? If I want to be popular, I need to take money away from all those programs that keep my friends and their companies from doing what they want. All government services should be ***pirate-ized***-I mean **privatized**."

"**NO, George, NO!** You can't chase an imaginary threat and remove money and regulations to do it. U.S. people will be so upset if you disable social programs by eliminating sources of funding."

GOT PRIVATIZATION? – The Guardian/UK, *Privatisation Won't Make You Popular*, by Kamil Mahdi, November 26, 2003

"Mr. Truth Fairy, when I'm President, the U.S. people won't have time to be upset with me. They'll be distracted with Boogeymen, and if they start paying attention to me, I'll create some new laws with my SuperDuper Invisible Ink pens to distract them some more."

"Name one law you might create, George."

"*Save the Forests*."

"And how will your SuperDuper Invisible Ink pens help?"

"Well, everyone will be happy with the law, but I'll use my SuperDuper Invisible Ink to write **DON'T** in front of the law!"

"Will you create any serious laws?"

"Sure. *Free Medicine for the Elderly*."

"Wow, George. You'll make medicine free for the older U.S. citizens?"

"No one wants to spend money on old people! I'll write an invisible **JUST KIDDING** in front of that law!"

"Is that all, George?"

"One more law. We'll make a law that gives people jobs. We'll call it: *Everybody can Work*."

"Don't tell me. You'll write **JUST KIDDING** with SuperDuper Invisible Ink after the law?"

"No, I wouldn't do that with that law."

"You wouldn't, George?"

"No, I'll write **NOT** with invisible ink in *front* of that law. Isn't that funny? It will be so much fun making laws when I'm President!"

"**NO, George, NO!** Just think of the negative impact your actions and laws will have on nature and people if you use your SuperDuper Invisible Ink pens. And what if some very smart people discover your Invisible Ink trick?"

GOT TRUTH ABOUT THE ENVIRONMENT? – New York Times, *Scientists Say Administration Distorts Facts*, by James Glanz, February 19, 2004

"Anyone who tells any of my secrets will be put in a jail far away so that no one can hear from him ever again."

"So anyone who leaks information ends up in jail?"

"Huh?"

"What will you do if someone tattles on you?"

"Oh. I'll tattle on him or put what my daddy's friends call "a spin" on the tattler's story."

"A spin, George?"

"I'll make up information about him and his family so that people will think they are all bad, bad people who belong in jail."

"So you'll jail anyone who disagrees with you or you'll ruin their reputation?"

"Sure. That's what I call justice."

"**NO, George, NO!** You can't possibly punish and jail everyone who disagrees with you! It's unconstitutional! Think of all of the jails that would be needed if U.S. Presidents did this. There simply isn't enough money for your game plan, George."

GOT NON-VIOLENT PROTESTERS DISGUISED AS TERRORISTS? www.americas.org - *Criminalizing Dissent: What Miami Means*, by Chris Jones, 11/26/03

GOT SANCTIONS? – Observer/UK, *Cold War Returns to US Backyard*, by Reed Lindsay, March 7, 2004

"The U.S. could run out of tax money to support all of your games, George. Where might you get more money?"

"Me and my friends will never run out of money, Mr. Truth Fairy. When money gets low, we'll just use the ***American Suppress credit card***. Besides, other countries will give us money, too, because they'll be afraid of all the weapons and power we have to fight the Boogeymen."

"The U. S. doesn't have its own **American Express credit card**, George. And the President of the United States doesn't control the world. What if people in other countries rise up to protest what you're doing?"

"Oh, my friends will be running countries all over the world. We'll be able to control how people act in these countries."

"George, what if countries are democracies? You won't try to run those places, will you?"

"Mr. Truth Fairy, if we want changes somewhere, we'll expect cooperation no matter what. If the leaders of the countries don't do what we want, we won't let those people buy food or medicine or other stuff until they do what we tell them to do. Daddy's friends call these ***spankins*** that we put on other countries."

"**Sanctions**, George."

"Oh, yeah. And we can put **sanctions** on any countries until we kill or chase out all the Boogeymen in that country."

"**NO, George, NO!** You can't do this. It's bad enough that you're planning to mess with the lives of the U.S. people. You also intend to control the citizens of our global community? It's as if you're tying to take over the world by making the U.S. a Super Power."

GOT WAYS TO MAKE OTHERS COOPERATE? – The Sunday Herald (Scotland), *Aristide's Final Hours*, by David Pratt, March 7, 2004

"We are playing *Let's Imagine*, Mr. Truth Fairy. I'm supposed to be imagining what I would do if I ruled the world, right?"

"But, George, I want you to imagine that you are the U.S. President, not the ruler of every human being. Besides, you and a few friends can't possibly run the entire world by yourselves."

"Well, Daddy says the CIA can do secret things that are really, really helpful to a President. They can find people or information, and they can help a President with plans to create special projects. I'll create a super secret project and call it… I know! I'll call it *The Project for a Few Americans in this Century*."

"Who will help you create your special project?"

"Well, of course, the CIA needs to help. And my friends and me will create an organization that takes stuff, and we'll call it the *Wonderful Taking Organization*. And we'll make a big bank to put all our money in, and we'll call that the *World's Bank* or the *Incredible Money Foundation*. Hey, we'll call them the *W.T.O.* and the *I.M.F.* for short."

"**NO, George, NO!** Your imagination is supposed to be used for the good of all people. Creating organizations and special projects just for you and your friends to run the entire world is simply selfish."

GOT A PROJECT FOR A NEW AMERICAN CENTURY? – The Nation, *The New American Century*, by Arundhati Roy, January 22, 2004

"Do you want to stop playing *Let's Imagine*, Mr. Truth Fairy?"

"Not yet, George. Why don't you explain how all of your ideas will work together?"

"Oh, it will be like an amazing dough machine. You put stuff in one side and then out pops money on the other side. Hey, that's funny, isn't it? Daddy says dough is another word for money."

"Simply hilarious, George. Tell me more about the machine."

"There will be a *HUGE MACHINE*. And it's a *Super Top Secret Machine*. It's so secret that it's invisible to everyone unless you know the *Super Secret Password*. And only my friends and the bosses in their corporations and world leaders who do what I want will know the password. I'll have secret meetings with the *WTO* and the *IMF* and my U.S. *PATROL* and military leaders to figure out what we can feed the machine. And the newspapers and TV won't talk about the machine."

"How can you possibly build such a **HUGE MACHINE** without everybody knowing about it, George?"

"Remember distractions, Mr. Truth Fairy? We'll keep telling people that there are *Boogeymen Everywhere*. So, they'll be too scared to travel or to look for the truth about this machine. And some of my friends will be *Super Secret Spies* to watch what people are reading in newspapers or on computers. If people start catching on or if they start talking…."

"Don't tell me. They'll be jailed, right? There are civil liberties, George! People have rights to look at the Internet and read books and move around freely."

"Yes, Mr. Truth Fairy. Lucky for me, I can change the laws when I'm the President! And Daddy's friends say that when people are really scared, they forget about their rights. Me and my friends will make people so scared of the Boogeyman popping up everywhere that they won't remember their rights."

"**NO, George, NO! STOP, George, STOP! GAME OVER!** This game is **OVER!** Your imaginary machine that uses your friend's money and corporations and special plans and the IMF and the WTO and the U.S. PATROL and the Military and the News Media and Super Secret Spies and new laws and sanctions and fear is amazing, but it's CRAZY. It must be fun to imagine money coming out of the system that is set up to work in this Super Top Secret machine. It's an incredible game plan that keeps average citizens fearful and in the dark. It is all really quite, quite clever, George, but it's wrong. **GEORGE W. BUSH, THE GAME IS OVER**."

GOT FEAR? – San Francisco Chronicle, *Fear Trumps Freedom In A Perpetual War*, by Harley Sorensen, January 19, 2004

"Am I in trouble?"

"George, you're not in trouble right now but the nation will be in big trouble if you rule the way you've planned. So we need to stop playing games now."

"You mean we can't play *Let's Imagine* anymore?"

"That's right, George. As your own personal Truth Fairy, I can see I have a lot of work to do before you are grown and become President. So, I need to get to work right away, and I need you to listen very closely because only children can see and hear truth fairies. What I'm telling you will be hidden in your heart when you're an adult, and you'll need to listen to your heart in order to remember my words and to make decisions as a President."

"I'll take time to listen when I'm President, Mr. Truth Fairy. I'll buy a ranch where I can go for a whole month to slow down and listen. And I'll invite my friends there to help me to remember you."

"But, George, you need to keep your inner truth fairy voice alive, and you can't rely on anyone else to do this for you. You need to take time daily to reflect on your goodness and the goodness of all people in order to remember me."

"Mr. Truth Fairy. I'm getting tired. I think I need a nap."

"George, you're in a dream. **No One Naps In Dreams**! Here, I'll make it really simple for you. I'm going to tell you the **Super Top Secret TRUTH**."

"A secret? Tell me! I love secrets."

"The only **Super Top Secret TRUTH** that exists has to do with **ONENESS**, George. We are all connected because we are the same. Every living being around the world, regardless of ability, age, sex, wealth, country of origin, or religious belief, is connected."

"The **Super Top Secret TRUTH** is about **ONENESS**, Mr. Truth Fairy?"

"**YES, George, YES**! We need to work hard to remember this truth. And when we remember this truth, we are incapable of thinking of fellow world citizens as Boogeymen. We won't hide truth to get people to do what we want, either. And love and cooperation, not greed, will guide us. Whether you are a President or a little child, you need to make sure you are being the kind of person that can remember this important truth. **ONENESS**. And as President, you must treat people as individuals and never support a machine that ignores the truth of oneness for any being. Your job as President is to spread the **Super Top Secret TRUTH** of **ONENESS**."

GOT A LEADER THAT NEEDS TO BE RE-PARENTED? – Time Magazine, *Confessions of a White House Insider*, by John F. Dickerson, January 11, 2004

GOT ONENESS? – "All men are caught in an inescapable network of mutuality, tied in a single garment of destiny."
-Martin Luther King, Jr.

"But if I do this, I can't fight Boogeymen or make a big machine or play cops and robbers all over the world or use tax money to fight wars or get rid of laws and regulations for my friends. I don't think I'll like being President."

"Oh, you'll be surprised, George. Leaders who have used the truth about **ONENESS** to guide them have loved life. If you focus on spreading the **Super Top Secret Truth** of **ONENESS** when you're President, you will enjoy every moment of your life. You'll leap out of bed in the morning, and you'll have purpose in every step. Life, with all of its ups and downs, will be joyful."

"But, Mr. Truth Fairy…. Hey, Mr. Truth Fairy! Where'd you go Mr. Truth Fairy?"

But the Truth Fairy was nowhere to be seen.

GOT A NEED FOR TRUTH FAIRIES IN YOUR LIFE? www.commondreams.org – www.forusa.org – *The Culture of Make Believe*, by Derrick Jensen, 2002

And George woke from his nap on his soft couch in his oval office in his big, white house. And he was no longer the young boy George.

"Mr. President, are you okay? The world leaders have gathered. It's almost time for your meeting," announced the President's secretary.

"I'm fine. I must have been dreaming. I can't remember what it was about but…I just need a moment alone before the meeting," said the President.

"Just need a moment, huh? You seem quite different today, Mr. President," mumbled the secretary as he closed the door.

"Different, huh? I actually feel the same." And as he said this, President George W. Bush walked over to the window, looked out at the beautiful trees that were just beginning to bloom and saw protesters in a large crowd outside his big, white house. He looked at the protestor's signs, he read what they said, and he smiled as he heard a faintly familiar song coming from the crowd:

Anything is possible
Remember this is true,
Who you are becoming
Is entirely up to you!

GOT TRUTH? – "He lives in wisdom who sees himself in all and all in him." - Bhavagad Gita

In Thanksgiving for all of the Truth Fairies in my life!

ISBN 0-9752834-1-3
Copyright ©2004 by Kathy Eder's Joy in Bloom
An Operation Hidden Agenda Production
Printed in China

Writer/Publisher   www.nogeorgeno.com
Illustrator   www.claytowne.com
Printer   www.overseasprinting.com

No!

No, George, No!

No!

No!

No!

No!

No!

No!